Contents

The Baker's Daughter   4

The Wonderful Weaver   9

King Grisly~Beard   17

He Wins
Who Waits   26

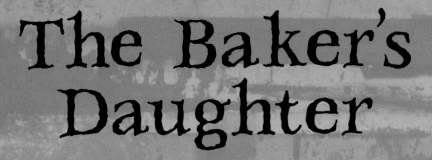

The Baker's Daughter

From *Folk-lore and Legends*
by Charles John Tibbits

ALONG TIME AGO, there lived a baker who was a mean, greedy man. He sought in every way to put money by, and cheated people whenever he was able when they came to his shop. He had a daughter who helped him in his business, and seeing how her father treated the people, and how he succeeded in getting money by his bad practices, she, too, in time came to do the like.

One day when her father was away, and the girl remained alone in the shop, an old woman came in. "My pretty girl," said she, "give me a bit of dough I beg of you, for I am old and very hungry."

The girl at first told her to be off, but as the old woman would not go, and begged harder than before for a piece of bread, at last the baker's daughter took up a piece of dough, and giving it to her, said: "There now, be off, and do not trouble me any more."

"My dear," said the woman, "you have given me a piece of dough, let me bake it in your oven, for I have no place of my own to bake it in."

"Very well," replied the girl, and, taking the dough, she placed it in the oven, while the old woman sat down to wait till it was baked.

When the girl thought the bread should be ready she looked in the oven expecting to find there a small cake, and was very much amazed to find instead a very large loaf of bread. She pretended to look about the oven as if in search of something. "I cannot find the cake," said she. "It must have tumbled into the fire and got burned."

"Very well," said the old woman, "give me another piece of dough instead and I will wait while it bakes."

So the girl took another piece of dough, smaller than the first piece, and having put it in the oven, shut the door. At the end of a few minutes or so she looked in again, and found there another loaf, larger than the last. "Dear me," said she, pretending to look about her, "I have surely lost the dough again. There's no cake here."

"Tis a pity," said the old woman, "but never mind. I will wait while you bake me another piece."

So the baker's daughter took a piece of dough as small as one of her fingers and put it in the oven, while the old woman sat near. When she thought it ought to be baked, she looked into the oven and there saw a loaf, larger than either of the others.

"That is mine," said the old woman.

"No," replied the girl. "How could such a large loaf have grown out of a little piece of dough?"

"It is mine, I am sure," said the woman.

"It is not," said the girl. "You shall not have it."

Well, when the old woman saw that the girl would not give her the loaf, and saw how she had tried to cheat her – for she was a fairy, and knew all the tricks that the baker's daughter had put upon her – she drew out from under her cloak a stick, and just touched the girl with it. Then a wonderful thing occurred, for the girl became all of a sudden changed into an owl, and flying about the room, at last, made for the door, and, finding it open, she flew out and was never seen again.

The Wonderful Weaver

From *Old Greek Stories* by James Baldwin

THERE WAS A YOUNG GIRL in Greece whose name was Arachne. Her face was pale but beautiful, and her eyes were big and blue, and her hair was long and like gold. All that she cared to do from morn till noon was to sit in the sun and spin, and all that she cared to do from noon till night was to sit in the shade and weave.

And oh, how fine and fair were the things which she wove in her loom! Flax, wool, silk – she worked with them all – and when they came from her hands, the cloth which she had made of them was so thin and soft and bright that men came from all parts of the world to see it. And they said that cloth so rare could not be made of flax, or wool, or silk, but that the warp was of rays of sunlight and the woof was of threads of gold.

Then as, day by day, the girl sat in the sun and span, or sat in the shade and wove, she said: "In all the world there is no yarn so fine as mine, and in all the world there is no cloth so soft and smooth, nor silk so bright and rare."

"Who taught you to spin and weave so well?" someone asked.

"No one taught me," she said. "I learned how to do it as I sat in the sun and the shade, but no one showed me."

"But it may be that Athena, the queen of the air, taught you, and you did not know it."

"Athena, the queen of the air? Bah!" said Arachne. "How could she teach me? Can she spin such skeins of yarn as these? Can she weave goods like mine?

I should like to see her try to match me. I can teach her a thing or two."

She looked up and saw in the doorway a tall woman wrapped in a long cloak. Her face was fair to see, but stern, oh, so stern! And her grey eyes were so sharp and bright that Arachne could not bring herself to meet her gaze.

"Arachne," said the woman, "I am Athena, the queen of the air, and I have heard your boast. Do you still mean to say that I have not taught you how to spin and weave?"

"No one has taught me," said Arachne, "and I thank no one for what I know." And she stood up, straight and proud, by the side of her loom.

"And do you still think that you can spin and weave as well as I?" said Athena.

Arachne's cheeks grew white, but she said: "Yes. I can weave as well as you."

"Then let me tell you what we will do," said Athena. "Three days from now we will both weave —

11

you on your loom, and I on mine. We will ask all the world to come and see us, and great Jupiter, who sits in the clouds, shall be the judge. And if your work is best, then I will weave no more so long as the world shall last. But if my work is best, then you shall never use loom or spindle or distaff again. Do you agree to this?"

"I agree," said Arachne.

"It is well," said Athena. And she was gone.

When the time came for the contest in weaving, all the world was there to see it, and great Jupiter sat among the clouds and looked on.

Arachne had set up her loom in the shade of a mulberry tree, where butterflies were flitting and grasshoppers chirping all through the livelong day. But Athena had set up her loom in the sky, where the breezes were blowing and the summer sun was shining, for she was the queen of the air.

Then Arachne took her skeins of finest silk and began to weave. And she wove a web of marvellous

beauty, so thin and light that it would float in the air, and yet so strong that it could hold a lion in its meshes, and the threads were of many colours, so beautifully arranged and mingled one with another that all who saw were filled with delight.

"No wonder that the maiden boasted of her skill," said the people.

And Jupiter himself nodded.

Then Athena began to weave. And she took of the sunbeams that gilded the mountain top, and of the snowy fleece of the summer clouds, and of the blue of the summer sky, and of the green of the summer fields, and of the royal purple of the autumn woods – and what do you suppose she wove?

The web which she wove in the sky was full of enchanting pictures of flowers and gardens, and of castles and towers, and of mountain heights, and of men and beasts, and of giants and dwarfs, and of the mighty beings who dwell in the clouds with Jupiter. And those who looked upon it were so filled with wonder and delight, that they forgot all about the beautiful web which Arachne had woven. And Arachne herself was ashamed and afraid when she saw it, and she hid her face in her hands and wept.

"Oh, how can I live," she cried, "now that I must never again use loom or spindle or distaff?" And she kept on, weeping and weeping and weeping, and saying, "How can I live?"

Then, when Athena saw that the poor maiden would never have any joy unless she were allowed to spin and weave, she took pity on her and said: "I would free you from your bargain if I could, but that is a thing which no one can do. You must hold to your agreement never to touch loom or spindle again. And yet, since you will never be happy unless you can spin and weave, I will give you a new form so that you can carry on your work with neither spindle nor loom."

Then she touched Arachne with the tip of the spear which she sometimes carried, and the maiden

was changed at once into a nimble spider, which ran into a shady place in the grass and began merrily to spin and weave a beautiful web.

I have heard it said that all the spiders which have been in the world since then are the children of Arachne, but I doubt whether this be true. Yet, for all I know, Arachne still lives and spins and weaves — and the very next spider you see may be she herself.

King Grisly-Beard

The Brothers Grimm

A GREAT KING of a land far away had a daughter who was very beautiful, but so proud and vain that none of the princes who came to ask her in marriage was good enough for her, and she only made fun of them.

The king held a great feast and invited all her suitors, and they all sat in a row – kings, and princes, and dukes, and earls, and counts, and barons, and knights. Then the princess came in, and as she passed them she said something spiteful to every one. The first was too fat: "He's as round as a

tub," said she. The next was too tall: "What a maypole!" said she. The next was too short: "What a dumpling!" said she. And thus she had some joke to crack upon every one, but she laughed more than all at a good king who was there. "Look at him," said she. "His beard is like an old mop – he shall be called Grisly-Beard." So the king got the nickname of Grisly-Beard.

But the old king was very angry when he saw how his daughter behaved, and how she ill-treated all his guests, and he vowed that, willing or unwilling, she should marry the first man, be he prince or beggar, that came to the door.

Two days after there came by a travelling fiddler, who began to play under the window and beg alms, and when the king heard him, he said, "Let him come in." So they brought in a dirty-looking fellow, and when he had sung before the king and the princess, he begged a boon. Then the king said, "You have sung so well, that I will give you my daughter for your wife." The princess begged and pleaded, but the king said, "I have sworn to give you to the first comer, and I will keep my word." So words and tears were no good. The parson was sent for, and she was married to the fiddler. When this was over the king said, "Now get ready to go – you must not stay here, you must travel on with your husband."

Then the fiddler went his way, and took her with

19

him, and they soon came to a great wood. "Pray,"
said she, "whose is this wood?"

"It belongs to King Grisly-Beard," answered he.
"Had you taken him, all this would have been yours."

"Ah! Unlucky wretch that I am!" sighed she. "I
wish I had married King Grisly-Beard!"

Next they came to some fine meadows. "Whose
are these beautiful green meadows?" said she.

"They belong to King Grisly-Beard, and they
could have been yours too," the fiddler replied.

"Ah! Unlucky wretch that I am!" said she. "I wish
I had married King Grisly-Beard!"

Then they came to a great city. "Whose is this
noble city?" said she.

"It belongs to King Grisly-Beard, and it could
have been yours."

"Ah! Unlucky wretch that I am!" sighed she. "I
wish I had married King Grisly-Beard!"

"Why should you wish for another husband?"
asked the fiddler. "Am not I good enough for you?"

At last they came to a small cottage. "What a paltry place!" said she. "To whom does that little dirty hole belong?"

Then the fiddler said, "That is your and my house, where we are to live."

"Where are your servants?" cried she.

"What do we want with servants?" said he. "You must do for yourself whatever is to be done. Now make the fire, and put on water and cook my supper, for I am very tired." But the princess knew nothing of making fires and cooking, and the fiddler was forced to help her.

When they had eaten a very scanty meal they went to bed. But the fiddler called her up very early in the morning to clean the house. Thus they lived for two days. When they had eaten up all there was in the cottage, the man said, "Wife, we can't go on thus, spending money and earning nothing. You must learn to weave baskets." Then he went out and cut willows, and brought them home, and she began to weave, but it made her fingers very sore. "I see this work won't do," said he. "Try and spin – perhaps you will do that better." So she sat down and tried to spin, but the threads cut her tender fingers till the blood ran. "See now," said the fiddler, "you are good for nothing – you can do no work! However, I'll try and set up a trade in pots and pans, and you shall stand in the market and sell them."

"Alas!" sighed she. "If any of my father's court should pass by and see me standing in the market, how they will laugh at me!"

But her husband did not care for that, and said she must work, if she did not wish to die of hunger. At first the trade went well. Many people, seeing such a beautiful woman, went to buy her wares, and paid their money without thinking of taking away the goods. They lived on this as long as it lasted, and then her husband bought a fresh lot of ware, and she sat herself down with it in the corner of the market, but a drunken soldier soon came by, and rode his horse against her stall, and broke all her goods into a thousand pieces. Then she began to cry, and knew not what to do. "What will become of me?" said she. "What will my husband say?" So she ran home and told him all.

"Who would have thought you would have been so silly," said he, "as to put an earthenware stall where everybody passes? But let us have no more crying. I have been to the king's palace, and asked if they did not want a kitchen-maid, and they say they will take you, and there you will have plenty to eat."

Thus the princess became a kitchen-maid, and she helped the cook to do all the dirtiest work, but she was allowed to carry home some of the meat that was left. She had not been working there long before she heard that the king's eldest son was passing by, going to be married, and she went to the window and looked out. All the pomp and brightness of the court was there. Then she grieved for the pride and folly which had brought her so low. And the servants gave her some of the rich meats, which she put into her basket to take home.

All of a sudden, as she was going out, in came the king's son in golden clothes. When he saw a beautiful woman at the door, he took her by the hand, and said she should be his partner in the dance, but she trembled for fear, for she saw that it was King Grisly-Beard, who was making fun of her. However, he kept fast hold, and led her in, and the cover of the basket came off, so that the meats in it fell about. She was so embarrassed that she wished herself a thousand feet deep in the earth. She sprang to the door to run away, but on the steps King Grisly-Beard overtook her, and brought her back. "Fear me not! I am the fiddler who has lived with you in the hut," he said. "I brought you there because I loved you. I am also the soldier that overset your stall. I have done all this only to cure you of your silly pride, and to show you the folly of your ill-treatment of me. Now all is over: you have learned wisdom, and it is time to hold our marriage feast."

Then the chamberlains came and brought her the most beautiful robes, and her father and his whole court were there already, and welcomed her home on her marriage. The feast was grand, they danced and sang, and all were merry – and I only wish that you and I had been at the party.

He Wins Who Waits

From Andrew Lang's *Olive Fairy Book*

ONCE UPON A TIME there reigned a king
who had an only daughter. The girl had
been spoiled by everybody from her birth, and,
besides being beautiful, was clever and wilful, and
when she grew old enough to be married she
refused to have anything to say to the prince whom
her father favoured, but declared she would choose
a husband for herself. By long experience the king
knew that when once she had made up her mind,
there was no use expecting her to change it, so he
enquired meekly what she wished him to do.

"Summon all the young men in the kingdom to appear before me a month from today," answered the princess. "The one to whom I shall give this golden apple shall be my husband."

"But, my dear—" began the king, in dismay.

"The one to whom I shall give this golden apple shall be my husband," repeated the princess, in a louder voice than before. And with a sigh, the king proceeded to do her bidding.

The young men arrived – tall and short, dark and fair, rich and poor. They stood in rows in the great courtyard in front of the palace, and the princess, passed before them all, holding the apple. Once or twice she stopped and hesitated, but in the end she always passed on, till she came to a youth near the end of the last row. There was nothing specially remarkable about him. A hundred others were handsomer, and all wore finer clothes, but he met the princess's eyes frankly and with a smile, and she smiled too, and held out the apple.

"There is some mistake," cried the king, who had hoped that none of the candidates would please her. "It is impossible that she can wish to marry the son of a poor widow! Tell her to look again!" and the princess went through the rows a second time, and gave the apple to the widow's son again. "Well, marry him if you will," exclaimed the angry king, "but at least you shall not stay here." And the princess answered nothing, but threw up her head, and taking the widow's son by the hand, they left the castle.

That evening they were married and after the ceremony they went back to the house of the bridegroom's mother, which was not much bigger than a hen-coop. The old woman was not at all pleased when her son entered bringing his bride with him. "As if we were not poor enough before," grumbled she. "I dare say this is some fine lady who can do nothing to earn her living."

But the princess stroked her arm, and said softly:

"Do not be vexed, dear mother, I am a famous spinner, and can sit at my wheel all day without breaking a thread."

The little family of three worked hard, but despite their efforts, they became poorer and poorer. At the end of six months it was agreed that the husband should go to a nearby town to get work. Here he met a merchant who was about to start on a long journey with a train of camels laden with goods of all sorts. The merchant took the widow's son as a servant, and gave him his whole year's salary beforehand. The young man returned home with the news, and next day bade farewell to his mother and his wife, who were very sad at parting from him.

"Do not forget me," whispered the princess as she flung her arms round his neck, "and as you pass by the well which lies near the city gate, stop and greet the old man you will find sitting there. Kiss his hand, and then ask him what counsel he can give you for your journey."

Then the youth set out, and when he reached the well where the old man was sitting he asked the questions as his wife had bidden him.

"My son," replied the old man, "remember three things: 'She whom the heart loves, is ever the most beautiful.' 'Patience is the first step on the road to happiness.' And 'He wins who waits.'"

The young man thanked him and went on his way.

Next morning the caravan set out, and before sunset it had arrived at the first halting place, round some wells, where another company of merchants had already encamped. No rain had fallen for a long while in that country, and both men and beasts were parched with thirst. To be sure, there was another well about half a mile away, where there was always water, but to get it you had to be lowered deep down, and, besides, no one who had ever descended that well had been known to come back.

Till they could store water in their bags of goat-skin, the caravans dared not go further, and the

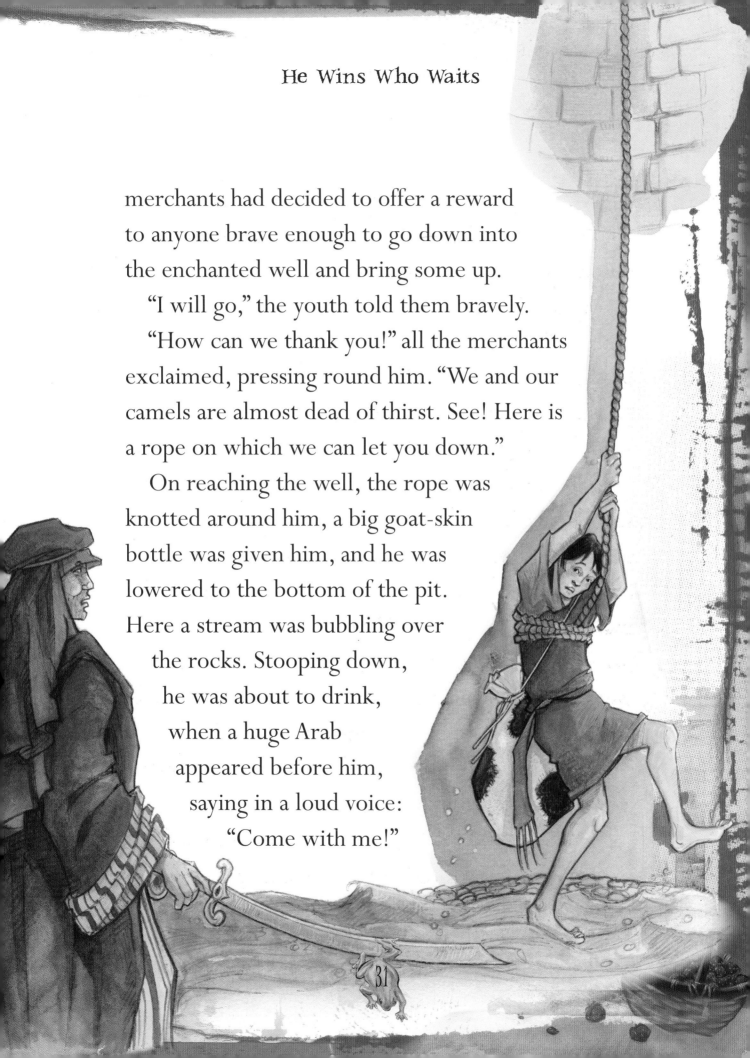

He Wins Who Waits

merchants had decided to offer a reward
to anyone brave enough to go down into
the enchanted well and bring some up.

"I will go," the youth told them bravely.

"How can we thank you!" all the merchants
exclaimed, pressing round him. "We and our
camels are almost dead of thirst. See! Here is
a rope on which we can let you down."

On reaching the well, the rope was
knotted around him, a big goat-skin
bottle was given him, and he was
lowered to the bottom of the pit.
Here a stream was bubbling over
the rocks. Stooping down,
he was about to drink,
when a huge Arab
appeared before him,
saying in a loud voice:
"Come with me!"

The young man rose, never doubting that his last hour had come, but as he could do nothing, he followed the Arab into a brilliantly lighted hall, on the further side of the little river. There his guide sat down, and drawing towards him two boys, he said to the stranger: "I have a question to ask you. If you answer it right, your life shall be spared. If not, your head will be forfeit, as the head of many another has been before you. Tell me: which of my two children do I think the handsomer."

The question did not seem a hard one, for while one boy was as beautiful a child as ever was seen, his brother was undoubtably ugly. But, just as the youth was going to speak, the old man's counsel flashed into the youth's mind, and he replied hastily: "The one whom we love best is always the handsomest."

"You have saved me!" cried the Arab in great joy. "I was condemned by a powerful, wicked genie to remain here until that riddle was answered correctly! Ah, if you could only guess how long I have suffered from the stupidity of all the people I have had to ask that question to! But what brought you to this place, and how can I reward you for what you have done for me?"

"By helping me to draw enough water for my caravan of eighty merchants and their camels, who are dying for want of it," replied the youth.

"That is easily done," said the Arab. "Take these three apples, and when you have filled your skin, and are ready to be drawn up, lay one of them on the ground. Halfway to the earth, let fall another, and at the top, drop the third. If you follow my directions no harm will happen to you. And take, besides, these three pomegranates, green, red and white. One day you will find a use for them!"

The young man did as he was told, and stepped out on the rocky waste, where the merchants were anxiously awaiting him. Oh, how thirsty they all were! But even after the camels had drunk, the skin seemed as full as ever.

Full of gratitude, the merchants pressed the money into his hands, while his own master bade him choose what goods he liked, and a mule to carry them.

So the widow's son had made his fortune at last, and when the merchant had sold his merchandise, and returned home to his native city, his servant hired a man by whom he sent the money and the mule back to his wife.

'I will send the pomegranates also,' thought he, 'for if I leave them in my turban they may some day fall out,' and he drew them out of his turban. But the fruit had vanished, and in their places were three precious stones, green, white and red.

For a long time he remained with the merchant, who gradually trusted him with all his business, and gave him a large share of the money he made. After twenty years, his master died and the young man set off to return home.

Now, soon after the young man had taken service

He Wins Who Waits

with the merchant a little boy had been born to
him, and both the princess and his old mother had
toiled hard all day to get the baby food and clothing.
When the money and the pomegranates arrived
there was no need for them to work any more, for
the princess saw at once that they were not fruit at
all, but precious stones of great value. She went to
the market and bought three of the finest
pomegranates she could find for her little boy to
eat. Then she bought beautiful new clothes for all of
them, and when they were dressed they looked as
fine as could be. Next, she took out one of the
precious stones which her husband had sent her. She
wrapped it up in a beautiful, embroidered
handkerchief and placed it in a small silver box.
Then she filled the old woman's pockets with gold
and silver pieces. "Go, dear mother," she said, "to the
palace, and present the jewel to the king, and if he
asks you what he can give you in return, tell him
that you want a paper, with his seal attached,

proclaiming that no one is to meddle with anything you may choose to do. Before you leave the palace, distribute the money amongst the servants."

The old woman took the box and started for the palace. No one there had ever seen a ruby of such beauty, and the royal jeweller declared to the king that there wasn't enough money in his treasury to buy it.

The dismayed king asked the old woman: "If I cannot give you its worth in money, is there anything you will take in exchange?"

"A paper signed by your hand, and sealed with your seal, proclaiming that I may do what I will, without let or hindrance," answered she promptly. And the king, delighted to have obtained what he coveted at so small a cost, gave her the paper. Then the old woman took her leave and returned home.

The fame of this wonderful ruby soon spread, and
envoys arrived at the little house to know if there
were more stones to sell. Each king was so anxious
to gain possession of the treasure that he bade his
messenger to outbid all the others. The princess sold
the two remaining stones for a sum of money so
large that if the gold pieces had been spread out they
would have reached to the moon. The first thing she
did was to build a palace by the side of the cottage,
and it was raised on pillars of gold, in which were
set great diamonds. Of course the news of this
palace was the first thing that reached the king, her
father, on his return from the wars, and he hurried
to see it for himself. In the doorway stood a young
man of twenty, who was his grandson (though
neither of them knew it), and so pleased was the
king with the appearance of the youth, that he
carried him back with him to his own palace, and
made him commander of the whole army.

Not long after this, the widow's son arrived in his

native land. There, sure enough, was the tiny cottage where he had lived with his mother, but the gorgeous building beside it was new to him. Not wishing to betray himself by asking questions of passing strangers, he climbed up into a tree that stood opposite the palace and watched, and waited.

A lady came out, and began to gather some of the roses and jasmine that hung about the porch. The twenty years that had passed since he had last beheld her vanished, and he knew her at once to be his own wife. He was about to jump down from the tree, when she was joined by a young man who placed his arm affectionately round her neck. At the sight of this the husband drew his bow, but the counsel of the wise man came back to him: 'Patience is the first step on the road to happiness.' And he laid it down.

At this moment the princess turned, and drawing her companion's head down to hers, kissed him on each cheek. A second time rage filled the heart of the watcher, and he snatched up his bow, when words, heard long since, seemed to sound in his ears: 'He wins who waits.' And the bow dropped.

Then, through the silent air came the sound of the youth's voice: "Mother, last night I dreamed that my father was here," said the youth. "How I wish it were true and I could meet him at last!"

Then the man understood, and he came down from the tree, and clasped his wife and son in his arms. All that night they talked, and when the sun rose it still found them talking. But as soon as it was proper, he went up to the palace to pay his homage to the king, and to inform him of all that had happened and who they all really were.

The king was overjoyed to think that his daughter, whom he had long since forgiven and sorely missed, was living at his gates, and was, besides, the mother of the youth who was so dear to him. "It was written beforehand," cried the monarch. "You are my son-in-law before the world, and shall be king after me."

And the man bowed his head. He had waited, and he had won.